She's a Good Skate,

Charlie Brown

Charles M. Schulz

SCHOLASTIC BOOK SERVICES
New York Toronto London Auckland Sydney Tokyo

ISBN 0-590-32329-6

12 11 10 9 8 7 6 5 4 3 2 1   2   2 3 4 5 6 7/8

Printed in the U.S.A.

Well, coach, what do you think?

There's no one harder to please
than a skating coach!

Problem number six . . . How many gallons of cream containing 25 percent butter-fat and milk containing 3½ percent butterfat must be mixed to obtain 50 gallons of cream containing 12½ percent butterfat? Ma'am, would you settle for twenty push-ups?

You look terrible, sir.

I can't stay awake, Marcie.
If you see me doze off, do
something to wake me.

I think you should try eating
a couple of eggs for breakfast, sir.

Do you think that might help me
stay awake, Marcie?

You've never seen
a chicken fall asleep
in class, have you?

That was a joke, sir.

Maybe you fall asleep in class because of an uncorrected astigmatism.

Oh, sure! You'd
love to see me
wearing glasses,
wouldn't you,
Marcie.

Some of us
think we look
kind of cute with
our glasses, sir!

Well, you've got it all wrong, Marcie. The reason I'm falling asleep in class is simple. I've been getting up every morning at 4:30 to practice skating.

That's crazy, sir. No one should have to get up at 4:30. Even the ice is still asleep at 4:30!

Hi, Chuck. It's me. I just want to let you know I'm here to wake up my skating coach.

Go back to sleep, Chuck.

Okay, coach, rise and shine!

Come on, coach,
let's put on your coat.

Well? What do you think of my routine, coach?

Are all skating coaches as crabby as you?

Okay, beautiful, get off the ice!
We're gonna play hockey.

Hockey? Get lost!
I was here first!

You wouldn't want to get hit with ten
hockey sticks, would you, beautiful?

Oh, yeah?
Come on and
try something!
Me and my
coach'll take
you all on.

That'll teach them! They can't mess around with my coach and yours truly!

Well, coach, back to work.

The only thing that keeps me going is the encouraging words of my coach.

I sure admire the way you can skate, sir.

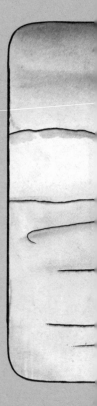

I'm working on my test figures, Marcie. There's a big competition coming up. It's my first.

You should try skating, Marcie.

I have weak ankles, sir.

There isn't any such thing.
Maybe my skating pro could
give you a few lessons.

He's crabby, but he's a good teacher.

I've never practiced
so hard in my life,
Marcie.

Doing well in this
competition really
means a lot to me.

Come on into my house,
sir. Have some hot
chocolate and cookies.

Marcie! You have
a sewing machine!

Why don't you make
me a skating outfit!

It's my mother's
machine, sir. And,
besides, I don't know
how to sew.

I want to look beautiful for the skating competition.

How about a red skating dress?

That's it! You can make me a red outfit with lots of sequins!

She's not much
for listening.

Come on, Marcie. Let's get some
great material for my costume.

Yes, ma'am, we want to buy some material for a skating dress. My little friend here has volunteered to make me a skating outfit for a competition. And before I forget, we'll need about a million sequins!

When I'm out there doing my
number, I want to really sparkle!

My stomach hurts
clear down to my toes.

Polyester double knit
is too expensive, ma'am.
How about denim?

I'll bet my friend here could make
me a neat skating dress out of denim.
She's a great sew-er!

See you tonight, Marcie.
Work hard on my costume.

Hi, Marcie. How's the sewing coming?

Well, the dress is finished. You should try it on and see how it fits.

I did the best I could, sir.
I just hope you like it.

How can I help but like
it? Just think, my own
special skating dress!

Maybe it'll look better after I get
the sequins on, sir.

MARCIE! This is the worst skating dress I've ever seen! It doesn't even have any sleeves in it! How can I skate in a dress like this? I'll be the laughingstock of the whole competition.

If you will recall, sir, I told you I didn't know how to sew.

I think I'm going to cry. I can feel the tears forming in my stomach.

Coach, look at this skating dress!

That stupid Marcie
has ruined everything.
What am I going to do?

When a skater is feeling low, she
should be able to cry on her pro's
shoulder. I can't even do that. . . .

You don't have any shoulders! ! !

Hey, coach! This looks very promising. Turn your head while I change.

How do I look?

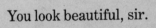
You look beautiful, sir.

There's only one
thing wrong . . . my hair.

How can I look beautiful when
I have hair that's mousey-blah?

If I'm gonna look beautiful for the skating competition, you'll have to help me with my hair.

Will all skaters
please clear the ice.

There are three things in life that people like to stare at: a flowing stream, a crackling fire, and a Zamboni clearing the ice.

First skater:
Miss Sandy.

Miss Evelyn.

Miss Peppermint Patty.

Her tape is broken! Without music, she's doomed.

YAY! HOORAY FOR
PEPPERMINT PATTY!

Well, coach, what did you think?

Don't you have anything
good to say?

Smack!